Children Around the World

They live in different countries.

Children Around the World

They are so different!

They have different ______________________

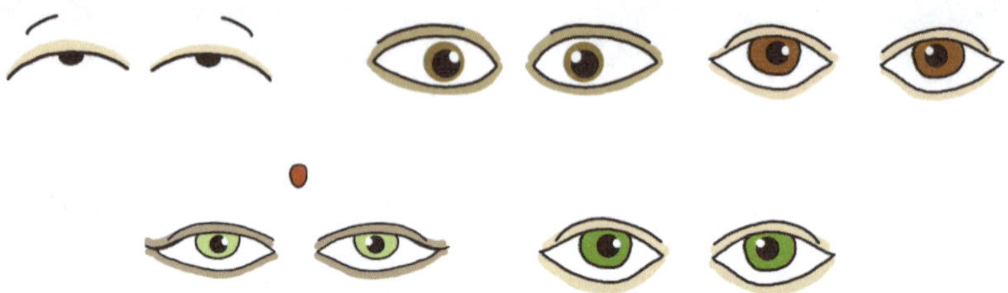

They have different ______________________

Children Around the World

They wear different

They eat different

Children Around the World

Look at these children.

Aiko

Tom

Felipe

Rajni

Dasha

Marco

Children Around the World

Where are they from?
Break the code and find out!

Felipe is from

Rajni is from

Dasha is from

Marco is from

Aiko is from

Tom is from the

Children Around the World

Can you find their countries on the map?

ITALY JAPAN INDIA

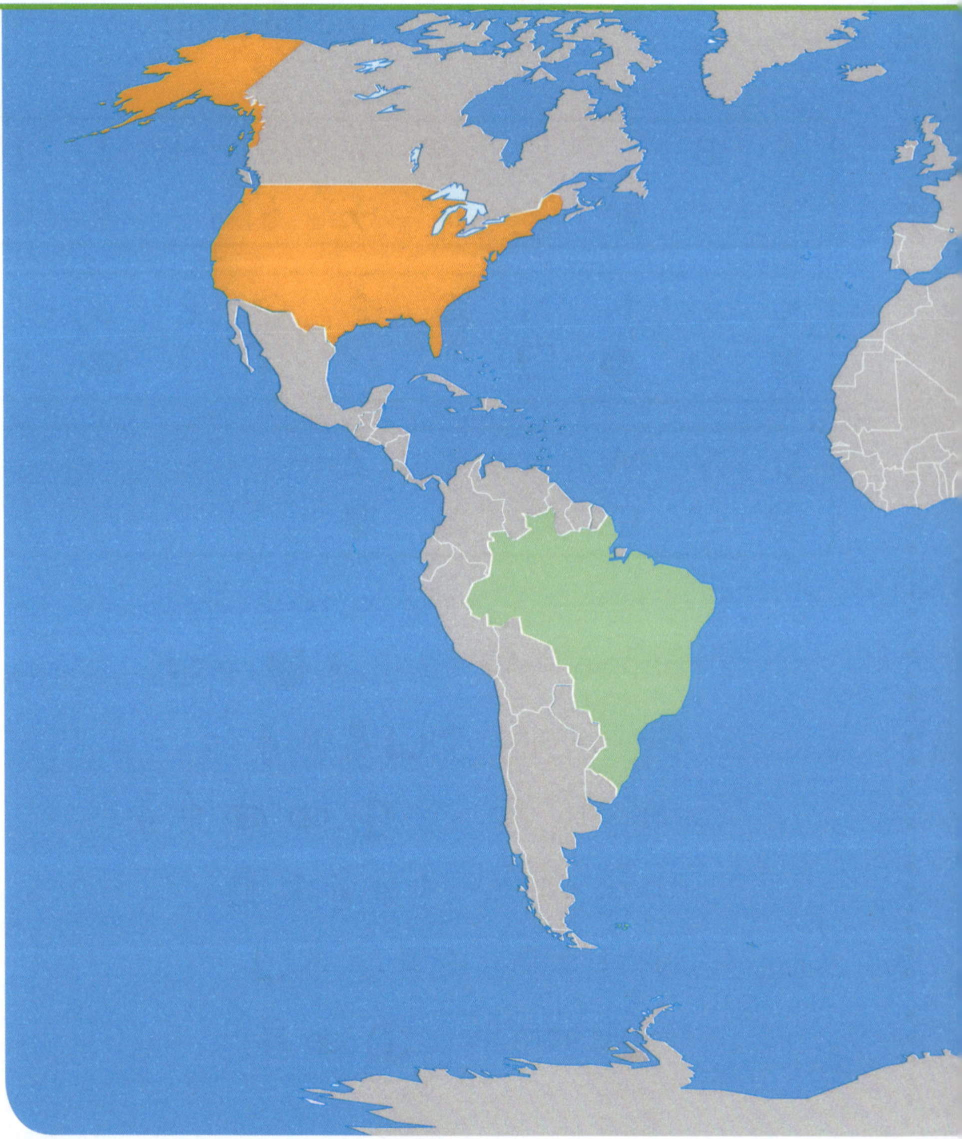

Children Around the World

Follow the colors and match.

RAZIL	THE USA	RUSSIA

Children Around the World

They speak different languages.

Children Around the World

Read and circle.

Aiko likes sushi.

Tom loves hamburgers.

Marco's favorite food is pasta.

Children Around the World

What's a popular food in your country?

Draw it here.

Children Around the World

They are different but they are all CHILDREN.

Complete the picture. Draw yourself and your friends.

And they all need:

Children Around the World

All about me!

My name is ______________________.

I am in ______________________. (**grade**)

My school is ______________________. (**name**)

My English teacher is ______________________

and my friends are ______________________

______________________ (**names**)

My year at school was:

☐ Very good! ☐ Good! ☐ Bad

Macmillan do Brasil
Rua José Félix de Oliveira 383
Granja Viana – 06708-645 – Cotia, SP, Brasil
Atendimento ao Professor: São Paulo – Capital (0XX11) 4613 2278
Demais localidades: 0800 168877
Fax: (0XX11) 4612 6098
E-mail: elt@macmillan.com.br
Visite nosso website: www.macmillan.com.br

INTERNAL CODE
978-66-7418-165-8
9786674181658